1, 2, 3
TO THE ZOO

a counting book by

ERIC CARLE

Hamish Hamilton
London

1

8 9 10 12

9 10 1 2 3 4

1 2 3 4 5 6

3 4 5 6 7 8

5 6 7 8 9 10

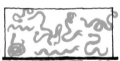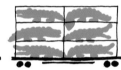

For Cirsten and Rolf

First published in America 1968 by The World Publishing Co., Cleveland and New York. First published in Great Britain 1969 by Hamish Hamilton Ltd., 27 Wrights Lane, London W8 5TZ Copyright © 1969, 1987 by Eric Carle. Reprinted 1972, 1976. Reissued with new artwork 1987 by Hamish Hamilton Ltd.
Printed in Hong Kong by South China Printing Co. British Library Cataloguing in Publication Data   Carle, Eric
1, 2, 3 To The Zoo   I. Title   813′.54   [J]   PZ7   ISBN 0-241-12360-7

3

5

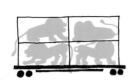

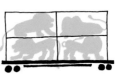

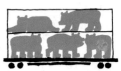

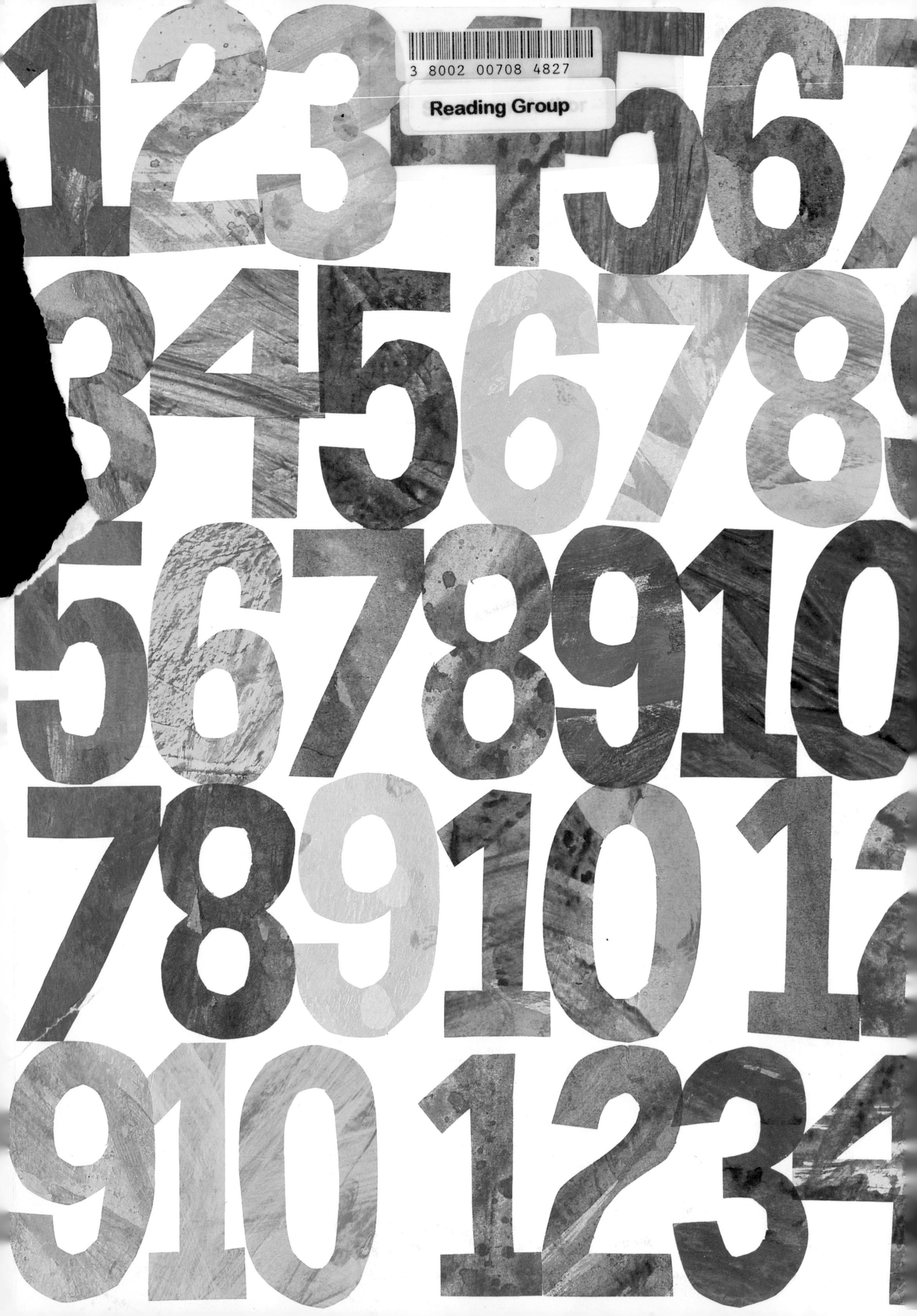